Key Stage 2

Adding and Subtracting

Steve Mills and Hilary Koll

Name _____

Schofield & Sims

Introduction

Understanding how addition and subtraction work is as important as knowing when and how to carry them out. In this learning workbook you will learn and practise different ways to add and subtract numbers using both mental and written methods. This is because trying each method will help you to build a better understanding of what is happening as you add and subtract.

How to use this book

Before you start using this book, write your name in the name box on the first page.

Then decide how to begin. If you want a complete course on addition and subtraction, you should work right through the book from beginning to end. Another way to use the book is to dip into it when you want to find out about a particular topic. The contents page will help you to find the pages you need.

Whichever way you choose, don't try to do too much at once – it's better to work through the book in short bursts.

When you have found the topic you want to study, look out for these icons, which mark different parts of the text:

Activities

This icon shows you the activities that you should complete. You write your answers in the spaces provided. You might find it useful to have some scrap paper to work on for some of the activities. After you have worked through all the activities on the page, turn to pages A1 to A3 at the centre of the book to check your answers. When you are sure that you understand the topic, put a tick in the box beside it on the Contents page.

On pages 10 and 16, you will find **Progress Tests**. These contain questions that will check your understanding of the topics that you have worked through so far. Check your answers on page A4. It is important that you correct any mistakes before moving on to the next section.

At the back of the book you will find a **Final Test**. This will check your understanding of all the topics (page 26).

Explanation

This text explains the topic and gives examples. Make sure you read it before you start the activities.

Scrap Paper

This icon tells you when you may need to use scrap paper to work out your answers.

Fascinating Facts

This text gives you useful background information about the subject.

Contents

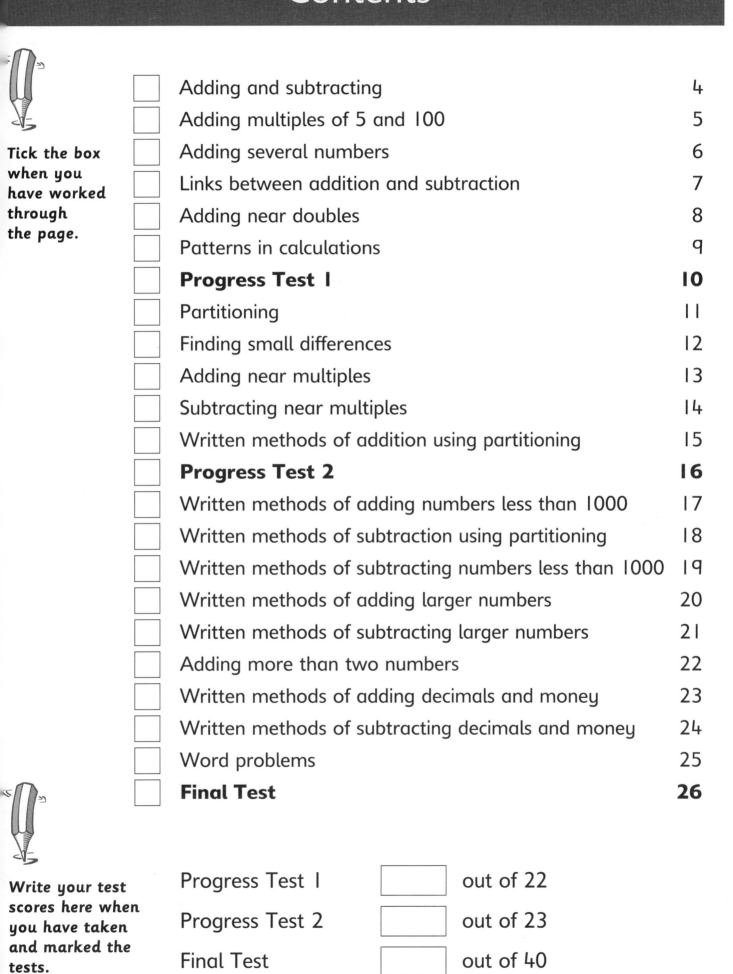

Tick the box when you have worked through the page.

Write your test scores here when you have taken and marked the tests.

Progress Test 1 ☐ out of 22

Progress Test 2 ☐ out of 23

Final Test ☐ out of 40

 **Did you know...?**

Addition is finding the total of two or more numbers.
We use a plus sign (+) when we add numbers together.

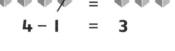

$$3 + 1 = 4$$

Subtraction is really two ideas.
The first is taking away one number from another.
The second is finding the difference between two numbers.

$$4 - 1 = 3$$

We use a minus sign (−) when we subtract numbers. $4 \overset{-3}{\frown} 1$

Subtraction is the opposite of addition and addition is the opposite of subtraction. If we add a number and then take it away we are left with the number we started with. $6 + 4 - 4 = 6$

Addition and subtraction words

These words often mean **add**:

(**plus**) (**more**) (**sum**) (**total**) (**altogether**) (**increase**)

These words often mean **subtract**:

(**take**) (**less**) (**minus**) (**left**) (**difference**) (**decrease**)

(**fewer**) (**take away**)

Other useful words to know

Multiples are numbers that are in times tables or beyond.

Multiples of 4 are 4, 8, 12, 16, 20, 24, 28, 32, 36, 40, 44, 48,... and they carry on and on.

Multiples of 5 are 5, 10, 15, 20, 25, 30, 35, 40, 45, 50, 55,...
Notice that multiples of **5** end with the unit digit **0** or **5**.

Multiples of 100 are 100, 200, 300, 400, 500,...
Notice that multiples of **100** end with two zero digits.

Adding multiples of 5

When adding multiples of **5**, add the tens digits first and then the units digits.

Remember that **5 + 5 = 10**

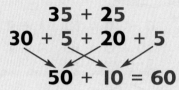

$$35 + 25$$
$$30 + 5 + 20 + 5$$
$$50 + 10 = 60$$

1. Add these multiples of **5**

a) 25 + 15 = _____   b) 15 + 35 = _____   c) 25 + 45 = _____

d) 45 + 35 = _____   e) 30 + 55 = _____   f) 65 + 25 = _____

g) 15 + 75 = _____   h) 35 + 60 = _____   i) 85 + 10 = _____

2. Fill in the missing numbers.

a) 25 + ☐ = 100   b) 45 + ☐ = 100

c) 65 + ☐ = 100   d) 80 + ☐ = 100

e) ☐ + 30 = 100   f) ☐ + 35 = 100

g) ☐ + 15 = 100   h) ☐ + 5 = 100

Adding multiples of 100

Multiples of **100** end with **00**. When adding multiples of **100**, think of each number in the question without the **00**, like this...

200 + 800 =   **200 + 800 = 1000**   **2 + 8 = 10**

3. Fill in the missing numbers.

a) 400 + 600 = ☐   b) 300 + 700 = ☐

c) 800 + ☐ = 1000   d) 900 + ☐ = 1000

e) ☐ + 500 = 1000   f) ☐ + 300 = 1000

Adding several numbers

 **Did you know...** You need to learn the facts below because they make adding several numbers easier.

0 + 10 = 10	1 + 9 = 10	2 + 8 = 10	3 + 7 = 10	4 + 6 = 10	5 + 5 = 10
10 + 0 = 10	9 + 1 = 10	8 + 2 = 10	7 + 3 = 10	6 + 4 = 10	

Adding three or more numbers

When adding three or more numbers, you can:

• find pairs that add to 10 and do these first:

so with $8 + 5 + 2$, just do $8 + 2 + 5 = 15$.

Or you can:
• start with the largest number first:

so with $3 + 4 + 9$, just do $9 + 3 + 4 = 16$.

1. Find the total for each row and column.

a)
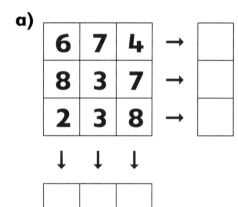

b)
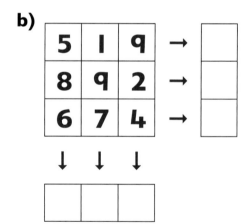

2. Find the total for each row and column.

a)
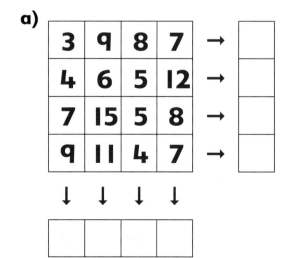

b)

4	7	5	5	→	
12	5	8	4	→	
3	16	7	4	→	
8	3	15	5	→	

↓ ↓ ↓ ↓

Inverses

Adding and subtracting are closely related.
They are opposites, because one 'undoes' the other.
The mathematical term for this is 'inverse'.
We say that addition and subtraction are **inverses**.

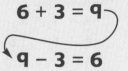

$6 + 3 = 9$
$9 - 3 = 6$

1. Follow the trains to find the answers, like this:

$$10 + 6 - 9 + 3 - 6 + 9 - 3 = \_\_\_\_$$

a)

10 | add **6** | subtract **9** | add **3** | subtract **6** | add **9** | subtract **3** ____

b)

17 | subtract **12** | add **8** | subtract **3** | add **12** | subtract **8** | add **3** ____

c)

25 | add **16** | subtract **10** | add **5** | subtract **16** | add **10** | subtract **5** ____

d)
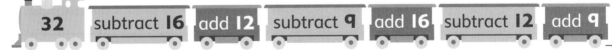

32 | subtract **16** | add **12** | subtract **9** | add **16** | subtract **12** | add **9** ____

2. What do you notice about each of your answers? Why do you think this is?

_____

_____

_____

3. Use these addition and subtraction facts to help you to answer the questions below.

| $31 + 17 = 48$ | $29 - 16 = 13$ | $23 + 15 = 38$ |

| $29 - 17 = 12$ | $14 + 28 = 42$ | $37 - 28 = 9$ |

a) $42 - 14 =$ _____ b) $28 + 9 =$ _____ c) $17 + 12 =$ _____

d) $13 + 16 =$ _____ e) $48 - 31 =$ _____ f) $38 - 15 =$ _____

Adding near doubles

Did you know...? Learning the doubles facts below will make many additions easier to do.

1 + 1 = 2	2 + 2 = 4	3 + 3 = 6	4 + 4 = 8	5 + 5 = 10
6 + 6 = 12	7 + 7 = 14	8 + 8 = 16	9 + 9 = 18	10 + 10 = 20
11 + 11 = 22	12 + 12 = 24	13 + 13 = 26	14 + 14 = 28	15 + 15 = 30

20 + 20 = 40	25 + 25 = 50	30 + 30 = 60	35 + 35 = 70
40 + 40 = 80	45 + 45 = 90	50 + 50 = 100	

Adding 'near doubles'

When we add numbers that are 'next to each other', like **6** and **7**, **9** and **10** or **15** and **16**, we can: **double one of the numbers and then add or subtract <u>one</u>.**

$$6 + 7 \rightarrow 6 + 6 + 1 = 13 \quad \text{or} \quad 7 + 7 - 1 = 13$$
$$9 + 10 \rightarrow 10 + 10 - 1 = 19$$
$$15 + 16 \rightarrow 15 + 15 + 1 = 31$$

Remember: If you doubled the <u>higher</u> number, <u>subtract</u> one.
If you doubled the <u>lower</u> number, <u>add</u> one.

1. Choose a number on the poster. Double your number, then add one and subtract one.

	19		34	
26		29		47
	23		39	
		43		37

Write your answers on scrap paper like this. Do this for all the numbers on the poster.

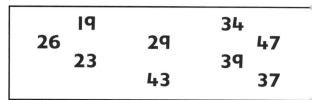

Double 26 = 52 ➚ 51 ➘ 53

2. Now use your answers to activity 1 to solve these 'near-double' questions.

a) 27 + 26 = _____

b) 34 + 35 = _____

c) 23 + 24 = _____

d) 19 + 18 = _____

e) 38 + 37 = _____

f) 44 + 43 = _____

g) 39 + 38 = _____

h) 47 + 48 = _____

i) 29 + 30 = _____

j) 270 + 260 = _____

k) 340 + 350 = _____

l) 380 + 370 = _____

m) 440 + 430 = _____

n) 180 + 190 = _____

o) 470 + 460 = _____

Patterns in calculations

Patterns in calculations

If you know one number fact then you can use it to work out others.
We can look for patterns in calculations.

If we know that	$16 + 3 = 19$
we can work out that	$16 + 13 = 29$ and $16 + 23 = 39$
If we know that	$5 + 10 = 15$
we can work out that	$5 + 100 = 105$ and $5 + 1000 = 1005$

1. Look for patterns to help you answer these questions.

a) $23 + 5 =$ _____

$33 + 5 =$ _____

$43 + 5 =$ _____

$53 + 5 =$ _____

b) $17 + 18 =$ _____

$17 + 28 =$ _____

$17 + 38 =$ _____

$17 + 48 =$ _____

c) $26 - 15 =$ _____

$36 - 15 =$ _____

$46 - 15 =$ _____

$56 - 15 =$ _____

d) $3 + 6 =$ _____

$30 + 60 =$ _____

$300 + 600 =$ _____

$3000 + 6000 =$ _____

e) $8 + 7 =$ _____

$80 + 70 =$ _____

$800 + 700 =$ _____

$8000 + 7000 =$ _____

f) $10 - 6 =$ _____

$100 - 6 =$ _____

$1000 - 6 =$ _____

$10\ 000 - 6 =$ _____

2. Look for patterns to help you fill in the missing numbers.

a)

+	1	2	3	4
1	2	3	4	5
2	3		5	
3	4	5		
4			7	

b)

+	6	8	10	12
4	10	12	14	
7	13	15		
10			20	
13	19			

Progress Test 1

1. Fill in the missing numbers.

a) 25 + ☐ = 100   b) 65 + ☐ = 100

c) ☐ + 40 = 100   d) ☐ + 55 = 100

e) 300 + ☐ = 1000   f) 600 + ☐ = 1000

2. Add these numbers.

a) 6 + 8 + 4 = _____   b) 3 + 9 + 6 = _____

c) 7 + 2 + 8 + 12 = _____   d) 4 + 14 + 6 + 11 = _____

3. Use these addition and subtraction facts to help you to answer the questions below.

| 36 + 19 = 55 | 38 − 17 = 21 | 29 + 14 = 43 |

a) 21 + 17 = _____   b) 43 − 14 = _____   c) 55 − 36 = _____

4. Add these numbers.

a) 29 + 28 = _____   b) 37 + 38 = _____   c) 43 + 44 = _____

d) 420 + 410 = _____   e) 380 + 390 = _____   f) 480 + 470 = _____

5. Look for patterns to help you answer these questions.

a) 26 + 5 = _____	b) 19 + 17 = _____	c) 9 + 7 = _____
36 + 5 = _____	19 + 27 = _____	90 + 70 = _____
46 + 5 = _____	19 + 37 = _____	900 + 700 = _____
56 + 5 = _____	19 + 47 = _____	9000 + 7000 = _____

Partitioning

 Did you know...? We can split numbers up to make adding them easier.
We call this **'partitioning'**.

- Split the numbers into tens and units
- Add the tens
- Add the units
- Add the two answers together

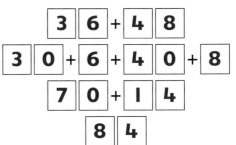

| 3 | 6 | + | 4 | 8 |

| 3 | 0 | + | 6 | + | 4 | 0 | + | 8 |

| 7 | 0 | + | 1 | 4 |

| 8 | 4 |

 **1.** Use the diagrams to add these numbers:

a)

| 2 | 5 | + | 5 | 4 |

b)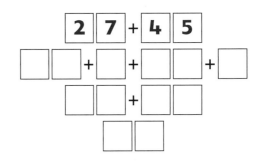

| 2 | 7 | + | 4 | 5 |

c)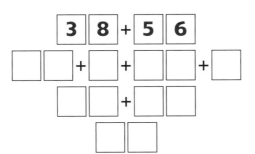

| 3 | 8 | + | 5 | 6 |

d)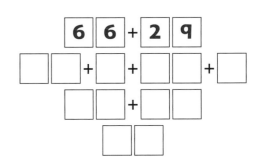

| 6 | 6 | + | 2 | 9 |

e)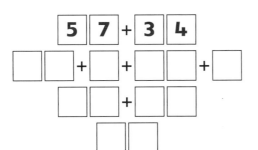

| 5 | 7 | + | 3 | 4 |

f)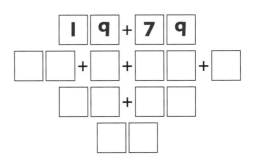

| 1 | 9 | + | 7 | 9 |

 2. Try these, using a similar method, in your head.

a) 24 + 58 = _____   b) 38 + 27 = _____   c) 27 + 62 = _____

d) 39 + 46 = _____   e) 43 + 48 = _____   f) 73 + 18 = _____

Finding small differences

Finding differences by counting on

We can find the difference between numbers by counting on.

Find the difference between 58 and 64:

Count on from **58** to **64:** 58   59   60   61   62   63   64

The difference between **58** and **64** is **6**

We can also use a blank number line, with **60** as a 'stepping stone':

       2 more   **4** more   **2 + 4 = 6**

    58   60   64

1. Find the difference between these numbers by counting on.

    a) 19 and 25 _____   b) 48 and 54 _____   c) 67 and 73 _____

    d) 78 and 86 _____   e) 85 and 96 _____   f) 97 and 104 _____

2. Answer these questions by counting on.

    a) $103 - 97 =$ _____   b) $206 - 198 =$ _____   c) $304 - 296 =$ _____

    d) $404 - 395 =$ _____   e) $407 - 396 =$ _____   f) $503 - 492 =$ _____

3. Use the blank number lines to find these differences.

    a) $406 - 394 =$ _____   b) $805 - 793 =$ _____

    394 _____ 406   793 _____ 805

    c) $1006 - 998 =$ _____   d) $2005 - 1997 =$ _____

    e) $3004 - 2993 =$ _____   f) $4008 - 3992 =$ _____

Adding near multiples

Adding near multiples of 10

To add numbers that are close to multiples of ten, like **59** or **48**, add the multiple of **10** and adjust afterwards:

$59 + 36 \rightarrow 60 + 36 = 96 \rightarrow$ subtract **1** $\rightarrow$ **95**

$56 + 31 \rightarrow 56 + 30 = 86 \rightarrow$ add **1** $\rightarrow$ **87**

$48 + 45 \rightarrow 50 + 45 = 95 \rightarrow$ subtract **2** $\rightarrow$ **93**

Think carefully about whether you need to adjust by adding or subtracting!

1. Add these numbers.

a) $47 + 19 = $ _____   b) $35 + 9 = $ _____   c) $53 + 29 = $ _____

d) $63 + 21 = $ _____   e) $19 + 74 = $ _____   f) $57 + 32 = $ _____

g) $11 + 125 = $ _____   h) $236 + 19 = $ _____   i) $354 + 21 = $ _____

j) $474 + 31 = $ _____   k) $49 + 527 = $ _____   l) $615 + 52 = $ _____

Adding near multiples of 100

You can use this method to add numbers that are close to multiples of **100**:

$439 + 99 \rightarrow 439 + 100 = 539 \rightarrow$ subtract **1** $\rightarrow$ **538**

$103 + 567 \rightarrow 100 + 567 = 667 \rightarrow$ add **3** $\rightarrow$ **670**

Think about whether you need to add or subtract.

2. Add these numbers.

a) $236 + 99 = $ _____   b) $362 + 99 = $ _____   c) $475 + 99 = $ _____

d) $346 + 101 = $ _____   e) $101 + 384 = $ _____   f) $475 + 102 = $ _____

g) $378 + 199 = $ _____   h) $537 + 199 = $ _____   i) $198 + 624 = $ _____

j) $647 + 201 = $ _____   k) $201 + 764 = $ _____   l) $865 + 202 = $ _____

Subtracting near multiples

Subtracting near multiples of 10

To subtract numbers that are close to multiples of ten, like **39** or **68**, subtract the multiple of **10** and adjust afterwards:

64 – 19 → 64 – 20 = 44 → add 1   → **45**

87 – 31 → 87 – 30 = 57 → subtract 1 → **56**

Think carefully about whether you need to adjust by adding or subtracting!

1. Subtract these numbers.

a) 54 – 9 = _____   b) 63 – 19 = _____   c) 67 – 29 = _____

d) 74 – 21 = _____   e) 86 – 21 = _____   f) 95 – 32 = _____

g) 127 – 19 = _____   h) 243 – 19 = _____   i) 354 – 42 = _____

j) 584 – 52 = _____   k) 675 – 39 = _____   l) 774 – 59 = _____

Subtracting near multiples of 100

You can use this method to subtract numbers that are close to multiples of **100**:

547 – 98   →   547 – 100 = 447 → add **2**   → **449**

675 – 103 →   675 – 100 = 575 → subtract **3** → **572**

Pay attention to whether you need to adjust by adding or subtracting.

2. Subtract these numbers.

a) 236 – 99 = _____   b) 264 – 99 = _____   c) 345 – 99 = _____

d) 367 – 101 = _____   e) 375 – 101 = _____   f) 453 – 102 = _____

g) 477 – 199 = _____   h) 653 – 299 = _____   i) 695 – 202 = _____

j) 734 – 302 = _____   k) 825 – 298 = _____   l) 783 – 397 = _____

Answers to Activities

Page 5

1. a) 40   b) 50   c) 70
   d) 80   e) 85   f) 90
   g) 90   h) 95   i) 95

2. a) 75   b) 55
   c) 35   d) 20
   e) 70   f) 65
   g) 85   h) 95

3. a) 1000   b) 1000
   c) 200   d) 100
   e) 500   f) 700

Page 6

1. a) row totals: 17, 18, 13
   column totals: 16, 13, 19
   b) row totals: 15, 19, 17
   column totals: 19, 17, 15

2. a) row totals: 27, 27, 35, 31
   column totals: 23, 41, 22, 34
   b) row totals: 21, 29, 30, 31
   column totals: 27, 31, 35, 18

Page 7

1. a) 10   b) 17   c) 25   d) 32

2. The answer is the same as the number you started with. For each addition there is a similar subtraction that undoes it and for each subtraction there is a similar addition that undoes it.

3. a) 28   b) 37   c) 29
   d) 29   e) 17   f) 23

Page 8

1. Answers on scrap paper in any order:

19	37	39
26	51	53
29	57	59
34	67	69
47	93	95
23	45	47
39	77	79
43	85	87
37	73	75

2. a) 53   b) 69   c) 47
   d) 37   e) 75   f) 87
   g) 77   h) 95   i) 59
   j) 530   k) 690   l) 750
   m) 870   n) 370   o) 930

Page 9

1. a) 28, 38, 48, 58
   b) 35, 45, 55, 65
   c) 11, 21, 31, 41
   d) 9, 90, 900, 9000
   e) 15, 150, 1500, 15 000
   f) 4, 94, 994, 9994

2. a)
2	3	4	5
3	4	5	6
4	5	6	7
5	6	7	8

   b)
10	12	14	16
13	15	17	19
16	18	20	22
19	21	23	25

Answers to Activities

Page 11

1. a) 79   b) 72
   c) 94   d) 95
   e) 91   f) 98

2. a) 82   b) 65   c) 89
   d) 85   e) 91   f) 91

Page 12

1. a) 6   b) 6   c) 6
   d) 8   e) 11   f) 7

2. a) 6   b) 8   c) 8
   d) 9   e) 11   f) 11

3. a) 12   b) 12
   c) 8   d) 8
   e) 11   f) 16

Page 13

1. a) 66   b) 44   c) 82
   d) 84   e) 93   f) 89
   g) 136   h) 255   i) 375
   j) 505   k) 576   l) 667

2. a) 335   b) 461   c) 574
   d) 447   e) 485   f) 577
   g) 577   h) 736   i) 822
   j) 848   k) 965   l) 1067

Page 14

1. a) 45   b) 44   c) 38
   d) 53   e) 65   f) 63
   g) 108   h) 224   i) 312
   j) 532   k) 636   l) 715

2. a) 137   b) 165   c) 246
   d) 266   e) 274   f) 351
   g) 278   h) 354   i) 493
   j) 432   k) 527   l) 386

Page 15

1. a) 388   b) 489   c) 589
   d) 579   e) 779   f) 799
   g) 879   h) 999   i) 999

2. a) 473   b) 647   c) 532
   d) 921   e) 713   f) 842
   g) 921   h) 902   i) 862

Page 17

1. a) 478   b) 378   c) 468
   d) 579   e) 589   f) 779
   g) 788   h) 878   i) 898

2. a) 401   b) 538   c) 619
   d) 635   e) 762   f) 933
   g) 852   h) 903   i) 967

Page 18

1. a) 422   b) 521   c) 513
   d) 315   e) 213   f) 221
   g) 222   h) 113   i) 342

2. a) 328   b) 382   c) 371
   d) 188   e) 188   f) 157
   g) 256   h) 57   i) 275

Answers to Activities

Page 19

1. a) 515   b) 411   c) 632
   d) 422   e) 212   f) 221
   g) 233   h) 121   i) 313

2. a) 572   b) 406   c) 591
   d) 77   e) 87   f) 169
   g) 69   h) 287   i) 289

Page 20

1. a) 44 699   b) 28 591
   c) 40 277   d) 99 076
   e) 70 214   f) 66 175

2. a) 94 396
   b) 112 680
   c) 54 578
   d) 170 282
   e) 80 496
   f) 111 490

Page 21

1. a) 35 522   b) 11 182
   c) 15 452   d) 17 845
   e) 8 603   f) 32 478

2. a) 5 517
   b) 13 569
   c) 17 746
   d) 28 861
   e) 44 164
   f) 2 443

Page 22

1. a) 375   b) 793   c) 2381

2. a) 3385   b) 7565   c) 7182

Page 23

1. a) 38·9   b) 61·9   c) 73·5
   d) 90·49   e) 90·03   f) 91·41

2. a) £60.97   b) £81.05   c) £83.29
   d) £90.59   e) £90.53   f) £101.43

Page 24

1. a) 21·5   b) 19·3   c) 16·8
   d) 16·91   e) 14·31   f) 5·86

2. a) £23.41   b) £20.89   c) £20.62
   d) £5.78   e) £8.49   f) £16.02

Page 25

1.   6839

2.   £2.58

3.   3187

Answers to Tests

PROGRESS TEST 1 – Page 10

1. a) 75 b) 35
   c) 60 d) 45
   e) 700 f) 400

2. a) 18 b) 18
   c) 29 d) 35

3. a) 38 b) 29 c) 19

4. a) 57 b) 75 c) 87
   d) 830 e) 770 f) 950

5. a) 31, 41, 51, 61
   b) 36, 46, 56, 66
   c) 16, 160, 1600, 16 000

Total marks = **22**

PROGRESS TEST 2 – Page 16

1. a) 93 b) 93

2. a) 7 b) 8
   c) 9 d) 12

3. a) 12 b) 12

4. a) 65 b) 66 c) 105
   d) 495 e) 595 f) 566

5. a) 64 b) 68 c) 36
   d) 166 e) 386 f) 374

6. a) 469 b) 639 c) 941

Total marks = **23**

FINAL TEST – Pages 26 to 28

1. a) 65 b) 400 c) 900

2. a) 18 b) 33

3. a) 38 b) 54 c) 19

4. a) 57 b) 750 c) 970

5. a) 7 b) 17

6. a) 106 b) 484 c) 771

7. a) 34 b) 484 c) 263

8. a) 583 b) 940

9. a) 397 b) 489
   c) 738 d) 1047

10. a) 422 b) 541
    c) 338 d) 248

11. a) 56 779 b) 50 001

12. a) 42 512 b) 25 643

13. a) 1030 b) 5680

14. a) 39·02 b) £62.29

15. a) 18·91 b) £5.94

16. 16 809

Total marks = **40**

Written methods of addition using partitioning

Written addition using partitioning

When numbers get too large to work with in your head you will
need a method for working on paper. When adding any numbers on
paper, make sure you line the columns up correctly and approximate first.
The method below uses partitioning to split up the numbers.
Start by adding the hundreds, then the tens and then the units.
Add these together:

326 + 471	H T U	Approximately **300 + 500 = 800**
	3 2 6	
	+ 4 7 1	
	7 0 0	(300 + 400)
	9 0	(20 + 70)
	7	(6 + 1)
	7 9 7	

1. Use partitioning to add these numbers.

a) 352 + 36 = _____   b) 426 + 63 = _____   c) 517 + 72 = _____

d) 428 + 151 = _____   e) 534 + 245 = _____   f) 316 + 483 = _____

g) 647 + 232 = _____   h) 718 + 281 = _____   i) 603 + 396 = _____

Written addition with carrying

This sum has some carrying. We can either start with the hundreds
or the units.   **637 + 285**

Either: **H T U**
```
    6 3 7     Approximately 600 + 300 = 900
  + 2 8 5
    8 0 0  (600 + 200)
    1 1 0  (30 + 80)
      1 2  (7 + 5)
    9 2 2
```

Or: **H T U**
```
    6 3 7
  + 2 8 5
      1 2  (7 + 5)
    1 1 0  (30 + 80)
    8 0 0  (600 + 200)
    9 2 2
```

2. Use partitioning to add these numbers.

a) 427 + 46 = _____   b) 572 + 75 = _____   c) 438 + 94 = _____

d) 634 + 287 = _____   e) 229 + 484 = _____   f) 673 + 169 = _____

g) 123 + 798 = _____   h) 503 + 399 = _____   i) 375 + 487 = _____

Progress Test 2

1. Use the diagrams to add these numbers:

a)
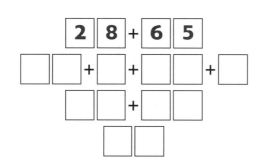

b)
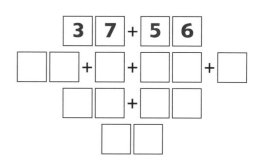

2. Find the difference between these numbers by counting on.

a) **39** and **46** _____   b) **57** and **65** _____

c) **305 − 296** = _____   d) **604 − 592** = _____

3. Use the blank number lines to find these differences.

a) **507 − 495** = _____   b) **706 − 694** = _____

_____   _____

4. Add these numbers.

a) **56 + 9** = _____   b) **47 + 19** = _____   c) **59 + 46** = _____

d) **364 + 131** = _____   e) **59 + 536** = _____   f) **477 + 89** = _____

5. Subtract these numbers.

a) **73 − 9** = _____   b) **87 − 19** = _____   c) **64 − 28** = _____

d) **365 − 199** = _____   e) **587 − 201** = _____   f) **672 − 298** = _____

6. Use partitioning to add these numbers.

a) **433 + 36** = _____   b) **456 + 183** = _____   c) **378 + 563** = _____

Written methods of adding numbers less than 1000

Written addition

When you are confident about partitioning, you can shorten the method.

326 + 471

```
  H T U
  3 2 6
+ 4 7 1
  7 9 7
```

Approximately 300 + 500 = 800

This calculation has no carrying.

1. Use this shorter method or one of your own to add these numbers.

a) 452 + 26 = _____   b) 356 + 22 = _____   c) 417 + 51 = _____

d) 318 + 261 = _____   e) 424 + 165 = _____   f) 516 + 263 = _____

g) 557 + 231 = _____   h) 617 + 261 = _____   i) 506 + 392 = _____

Written addition with carrying

568 + 274   *Approximately 550 + 300 = 850*

This calculation has lots of carrying so it is best to start with the units. Follow the boxes if you're not sure.

```
    H   T   U
    5   6   8
+   2   7   4
    8   4   2
    I   I
```

| 5+2+1=8 Write **8** | 6+7+1=14 Write **4** and carry **I** hundred into the hundreds column. | 8+4=12 Write **2** and carry **I** ten into the tens column. |

2. Use this method or one of your own to add these numbers.

a) 372 + 29 = _____   b) 485 + 53 = _____   c) 537 + 82 = _____

d) 367 + 268 = _____   e) 573 + 189 = _____   f) 547 + 386 = _____

g) 658 + 194 = _____   h) 509 + 394 = _____   i) 689 + 278 = _____

Written subtraction using partitioning

When subtracting large numbers on paper make sure you line the columns up correctly and approximate first.

746 – 432

H	T	U
7	4	6
– 4	3	2

→   700+40+6
     – 400+30+2
     300+10+4   = 314

Approximately **700 – 400 = 300**

Check your answer by **adding** the last two rows **432+314 = 746**

I. Use partitioning to subtract these numbers.

a) 475 – 53 = _____   b) 568 – 47 = _____   c) 589 – 76 = _____

d) 538 – 223 = _____   e) 569 – 356 = _____   f) 746 – 525 = _____

g) 683 – 461 = _____   h) 858 – 745 = _____   i) 963 – 621 = _____

Written subtraction with exchanges

637 – 275   Approximately **600 – 300 = 300**

This calculation needs exchanges. Follow the arrows to see how these happen.

H	T	U
6	3	7
– 2	7	5

→   600+30+7   →   500+130+7
   – 200+70+5   – 200+ 70+5
              300+ 60+2 = 362

Notice that we have changed **600 + 30** into **500 + 130**
This makes it easier to subtract the **70** in **275**

2. Use this method or one of your own to subtract these numbers.

a) 385 – 57 = _____   b) 428 – 46 = _____   c) 463 – 92 = _____

d) 472 – 284 = _____   e) 564 – 376 = _____   f) 741 – 584 = _____

g) 623 – 367 = _____   h) 753 – 696 = _____   i) 964 – 689 = _____

Written subtraction

When you are confident about partitioning, you can shorten the method.

647 – 432

```
H T U
6 4 7
– 4 3 2
  2 1 5
```

Approximately **600 – 400 = 200**

This calculation has no exchange.

Check your answer by **adding** the last two rows **432+215 = 647**

1. Use this shorter method or one of your own to subtract these numbers.

a) 578 – 63 = _____ b) 484 – 73 = _____ c) 689 – 57 = _____

d) 658 – 236 = _____ e) 669 – 457 = _____ f) 693 – 472 = _____

g) 656 – 423 = _____ h) 845 – 724 = _____ i) 989 – 676 = _____

Written subtraction with exchanges

This calculation needs exchanges. Follow the boxes if you're not sure.

642 – 275 Approximately **600 – 300 = 300**

```
 H      T      U
 ⁵6̸    ⁴3̸¹3   ¹2
–  2     7      5
   3     6      7
```

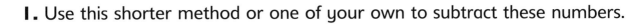

| 5–2=3 Write **3** in the hundreds column. | 3–7 we can't do, so change **1** of the hundreds into **10** tens. The **3** becomes **13**. Take **7** from **13**. Write **6** in the tens column. | 2–5 we can't do, so change **1** of the tens into **10** units. Cross out a ten, leaving **3** tens. The **2** becomes **12**. Take **5** from **12**. Write **7** in the units column. |

2. Use this shorter method or one of your own to subtract these numbers.

a) 625 – 53 = _____ b) 453 – 47 = _____ c) 685 – 94 = _____

d) 473 – 396 = _____ e) 463 – 376 = _____ f) 628 – 459 = _____

g) 637 – 568 = _____ h) 832 – 545 = _____ i) 917 – 628 = _____

Adding larger numbers

This calculation has lots of carrying! Follow the boxes if you're not sure.

46 538 + 25 907 *Approximately **45 000 + 25 000 = 70 000***

	TTh	Th	H	T	U
	4	6	5	3	8
+	2	5	9	0	7
	7	2	4	4	5
	1	1		1	

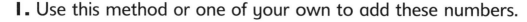

4+2+1=7 Write **7** in the ten thousands column.	6+5+1=12 Write **2** and carry **1** ten thousand.	5+9=14 Write **4** and carry **1** thousand into the thousands column.	3+0+1=4 Write **4** in the tens column.	8+7=15 Write **5** and carry **1** ten into the tens column.

1. Use this method or one of your own to add these numbers.

a) **42 323 + 2 376** = _____ b) **5 356 + 23 235** = _____

c) **34 815 + 5 462** = _____ d) **53 729 + 45 347** = _____

e) **28 693 + 41 521** = _____ f) **38 938 + 27 237** = _____

2. Here is a list of the number of people who went to the cinema to watch two different films in April.

Week	Space Frontier	Hold Up
1	37 687	42 809
2	56 709	69 871
3	35 092	78 278
4	19 486	92 004

How many people in total:

a) saw Space Frontier in weeks **1** and **2**? _____

b) saw Hold Up in weeks **1** and **2**? _____

c) saw Space Frontier in weeks **3** and **4**? _____

d) saw Hold Up in weeks **3** and **4**? _____

e) went to the cinema in week **1**? _____

f) went to the cinema in week **4**? _____

Subtracting larger numbers

This calculation needs exchanges. Follow the boxes if you're not sure.

75 634 – 43 716   *Approximately* **70 000 – 40 000 = 30 000**

	TTh	Th	H	T	U
	7	~~5~~ 4	'6	~~3~~ 2	'4
–	4	3	7	1	6
	3	1	9	1	8

7 – 4 = 3 Write **3** in the ten thousands column.	4 – 3 = 1 Write **1** in the thousands column.	6 – 7 we can't do, so change **1** thousand into **10** hundreds. Cross out **1** of the thousands. Take **7** from **16**. Write **9** in the hundreds column.	2 – 1 = 1 Write **1** in the tens column.	4 – 6 we can't do, so change **1** ten into **10** units. Cross out **1** of the tens. The **4** becomes **14**. Take **6** from **14**. Write **8** in the units column.

1. Use this method or one of your own to subtract these numbers.

a) **37 867 – 2 345** = _____

b) **45 756 – 34 574** = _____

c) **54 914 – 39 462** = _____

d) **63 629 – 45 784** = _____

e) **66 251 – 57 648** = _____

f) **71 452 – 38 974** = _____

2. Here is a list of attendances from some football matches.

match **1**	Liverpool v Arsenal	46 829
match **2**	Birmingham v Everton	37 054
match **3**	Man United v Spurs	67 649
match **4**	Newcastle U v Bolton W	52 346
match **5**	Aston Villa v Chelsea	49 903
match **6**	Blackburn R v Southampton	23 485

Remember to put the larger number first!

Find the difference between the attendances at these matches.

a) match **1** and match **4** _____

b) match **2** and match **6** _____

c) match **3** and match **5** _____

d) match **4** and match **6** _____

e) match **3** and match **6** _____

f) match **5** and match **4** _____

Adding more than two numbers

We can add as many numbers as we like, as long as we line up the numbers so that each digit is in the correct column. Make sure the units all line up correctly.

586 + 3154 + 472 + 2837   *Approx.* **600 + 3000 + 500 + 3000 = 7100**

```
   Th  H  T  U
       5  8  6
    3  1  5  4
       4  7  2
 +  2  8  3  7
    7  0  4  9
    2  2  1
```

Tip: Look for pairs of digits that add to **10**, such as **7** and **3**, or **6** and **4**, etc.

1. Add these numbers, approximating first.

a) 257+ 32 + 86   **b) 37 +203+553**   **c) 627+1476+278**

Approximation: *Approximation:*   *Approximation:*

```
   H  T  U
   2  5  7
      3  2
 +    8  6
 _____
```

```
   H  T  U
      3  7
   2  0  3
 + 5  5  3
 _____
```

```
 Th  H  T  U
     6  2  7
  1  4  7  6
 +   2  7  8
 _____
```

2. Approximate first, then line up the numbers and find the total.

a) 2746 + 475 + 164   **b) 456 + 2785 + 4324**   **c) 5786 + 442 + 95**

Approximation: *Approximation:*   *Approximation:*

```
 Th  H  T  U
  2  7  4  6


 +
 _____
```

```
 Th  H  T  U



 _____
```

```
 Th  H  T  U



 _____
```

Written methods of adding decimals and money

Did you know...?

We can add decimals in the same way we add whole numbers.
Just make sure to line up the decimal points.

58·6 + 31·2

```
  T  U · t      Approx. 59 + 31 = 90
  5  8 · 6
+ 3  1 · 2
  8  9 · 8
```

15·74 + 23·87

```
  T  U · t  h    Approx. 16 + 24 = 40
  1  5 · 7  4
+ 2  3 · 8  7
  3  9 · 6  1
```

When you are adding decimals it is very important to get an approximate answer
first to make sure the decimal point is in the right place.

1. Add these numbers.

a)
```
  2 5·7
+ 1 3·2
```

b)
```
  3 6·6
+ 2 5·3
```

c)
```
  4 5·7
+ 2 7·8
```

d)
```
  5 3·6 5
+ 3 6·8 4
```

e)
```
  6 2·0 8
+ 2 7·9 5
```

f)
```
  7 4·9 2
+ 1 6·4 9
```

Did you know...?

We can add money in the same way that we add decimals with **2** places.

£24.65 + £13.86

```
  T  U . t  h      Approx. £25 + £14 = £39
  2  4 . 6  5
+ 1  3 . 8  6
  3  8 . 5  1   →   £38.51
```

2. Add these amounts of money.

a)
```
  £ 3 6.7 1
+ £ 2 4.2 6
```

b)
```
  £ 4 5.6 7
+ £ 3 5.3 8
```

c)
```
  £ 5 5.4 7
+ £ 2 7.8 2
```

d)
```
  £ 6 3.8 5
+ £ 2 6.7 4
```

e)
```
  £ 7 2.5 8
+ £ 1 7.9 5
```

f)
```
  £ 7 4.9 7
+ £ 2 6.4 6
```

Written methods of subtracting decimals and money

Did you know...

We can subtract decimals in the same way we subtract whole numbers. Just make sure to line up the decimal points.

76·8 – 54·3

```
  T  U · t    Approx. 77 – 54 = 23
  7  6 · 8
- 5  4 · 3
  2  2 · 5
```

47·58 – 21·79

```
  T  U · t  h   Approx. 48 – 22 = 26
  4  7 · 5  8
- 2  1 · 7  9
  2  5 · 7  9
```

Check your answer by **adding** the bottom two lines of the calculations.

1. Subtract these numbers.

a)
```
    3 6·7
  - 1 5·2
```

b)
```
    3 8·6
  - 1 9·3
```

c)
```
    4 5·6
  - 2 8·8
```

d)
```
    5 6·7 5
  - 3 9·8 4
```

e)
```
    6 2·1 9
  - 4 7·8 8
```

f)
```
    7 2·7 5
  - 6 6·8 9
```

Did you know...

We can subtract money in the same way that we subtract decimals with **2** places.

£47.38 – 29.87

```
  T  U . t  h      Approx. £47 – £30 = £17
  4  7 . 3  8
- 2  9 . 8  7
  1  7 . 5  1   →   £17.51
```

2. Subtract these amounts of money.

a)
```
  £ 4 7.7 2
- £ 2 4.3 1
```

b)
```
  £ 5 3.2 7
- £ 3 2.3 8
```

c)
```
  £ 5 8.4 3
- £ 3 7.8 1
```

d)
```
  £ 6 9.2 3
- £ 6 3.4 5
```

e)
```
  £ 7 6.1 8
- £ 6 7.6 9
```

f)
```
  £ 9 5.0 1
- £ 7 8.9 9
```

Word problems

Solving word problems

When faced with a problem, follow these steps:

- Read the problem carefully.

- Look for any useful words in the question.

- Write down any important numbers in the question.

- Decide how to work it out.

- Get an approximate answer, work it out, then check.

43 people were on the bus. At the next stop 24 got off but 18 more got on. How many people were on the bus now?

- Important numbers **43, 24, 18**

- Subtract **24** from **43** and then add **18**

Work it out : **43 − 24 = 19, 19 + 18 = 37**

Approximately:

40 − 20 + 20 = 40

1. **9543** people visited the Coliseum cinema this year.

   This was **2704** more than last year.

   How many people visited the cinema last year?

2. Dan buys a bag of crisps for **39**p,
   a drink for **34**p and a magazine for £**1.69**

   How much change does he get from £**5**?

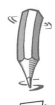

3. A car park has **12 785** spaces. **9598** are empty.

   How many cars are in the car park?

Final Test

1. Fill in the missing numbers.

   a) 35 + ☐ = 100   **b)** 600 + ☐ = 1000   **c)** ☐ + 100 = 1000

2. Add these numbers.

   a) 4 + 8 + 6 = _____   **b)** 13 + 9 + 7 + 4 = _____

3. Use these addition and subtraction facts to help you to answer the questions below.

45 + 19 = 64	54 − 18 = 36	38 + 17 = 55

   a) 55 − 17 = _____   **b)** 36 + 18 = _____   **c)** 64 − 45 = _____

4. Add these numbers.

   a) 29 + 28 = _____   **b)** 370 + 380 = _____   **c)** 480 + 490 = _____

5. Find the difference between these numbers by counting on.

   a) 39 and 46 _____   **b)** 708 and 691 _____

6. Add these numbers.

   a) 77 + 29 = _____   **b)** 365 + 119 = _____   **c)** 273 + 498 = _____

7. Subtract these numbers.

   a) 63 − 29 = _____   **b)** 683 − 199 = _____   **c)** 361 − 98 = _____

8. Use partitioning to add these numbers. Show your working in the space provided.

a) **527 + 56 =** _____

b) **653 + 287 =** _____

9. Add these numbers.

a) **372 + 25 =** _____

b) **436 + 53 =** _____

c) **473 + 265 =** _____

d) **568 + 479 =** _____

10. Subtract these numbers.

a) **475 − 53 =** _____

b) **587 − 46 =** _____

c) **724 − 386 =** _____

d) **841 − 593 =** _____

11. Add these numbers.

a) **53 347 + 3 432 =** _____

b) **6 326 + 43 675 =** _____

12. Subtract these numbers.

a) **46 859 − 4 347** = _____

b) **54 217 − 28 574** = _____

13. Add these numbers.

a) **28 + 835 + 167** = _____

b) **3207 + 2059 + 331 + 83** = _____

14. Answer these questions.

a)
```
    2 6·7 4
+   1 2·2 8
_____
```

b)
```
  £ 2 7.7 3
+ £ 3 4.5 6
_____
```

15. Answer these questions.

a)
```
    3 7·7 5
−   1 8·8 4
_____
```

b)
```
  £ 5 3.5 6
− £ 4 7.6 2
_____
```

16. Solve this problem.

12 948 people visited the Atlas theme park this year.

This was **3861** less than last year.

How many people visited the theme park last year? _____